ea as in br**ea**d

• Write and say **ea** _ea_ **ea** _____ **ea** _____ **ea** _____

• Add **ea** to make fourteen words.

(br) (d) _____   (inst) (d) _____
(d) (f) _____   (h) (d) _____
(h) **ea** (vy) _____ (tr) **ea** (sure) _____
(d) (d) _____   (r) (d) _____

(f) (ther) _____   (l) (ther) _____
(m) **ea** (sure) _____ (w) **ea** (pon) _____
(w) (lth) _____   (w) (ther) _____

• Write the correct word under each picture.

_____ _____ _____ _____

• Use words you have made to complete these sentences.

Our teacher _____ a funny story to the class.

A sword is a _____, so is a knife.

Your _____ is above your neck.

I can't go swimming now. I'll go tomorrow _____ .

The pirates hid the _____ on an island.

• **Word Puzzle**

a lot of money   ◯(e)(a)◯◯◯

not alive   ◯(e)(a)◯

shoes and boots
may be made of this   ◯(e)(a)◯◯◯◯

cannot hear   ◯(e)(a)◯

as light as a   ◯(e)(a)◯◯◯

3

bread _bread_

deaf _____

head _____

wealth _____

dead _____

heavy _____

read _____

instead

_____

weapon

_____

leather

_____

feather

_____

treasure

_____

measure

_____

weather

_____

 **cl-** as in **cl**ock

Write and say **cl** _cl_ cl _____ cl _____ cl _____

Add **cl** to make sixteen words.

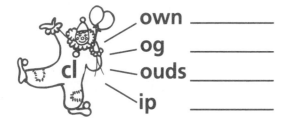
cl — **own** _____
— **og** _____
— **ouds** _____
— **ip** _____

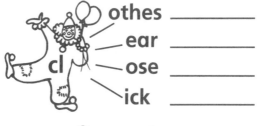
cl — **othes** _____
— **ear** _____
— **ose** _____
— **ick** _____

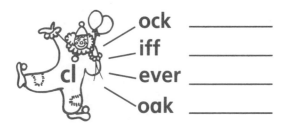
cl — **ock** _____
— **iff** _____
— **ever** _____
— **oak** _____

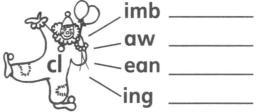
cl — **imb** _____
— **aw** _____
— **ean** _____
— **ing** _____

Write the correct word under each picture.

_____ _____ _____ _____ _____

Use words you have made to complete these sentences.

A _____ does funny things at the circus.

Firemen often _____ high ladders to put out fires.

We knew it would rain when we saw
the black _____.

If you are _____, you are quick to learn.

Be very careful! Do not cross the
road unless it is _____.

Word Puzzle

small, sharp sound
opposite of dirty
hold tightly to something
fastener for the hair or paper
coat without sleeves
opposite of open
easy to see through

c	l			
c	l			
c	l			
c	l			
c	l			
c	l			
c	l			

clog _clog_

cliff _____

clown _____

climb _____

clouds _____

clever _____

clear _____

click _____

clean _____

clip _____

cloak _____

close _____

claw _____

cling _____

clock _____

clothes

_____

gl- as in glass

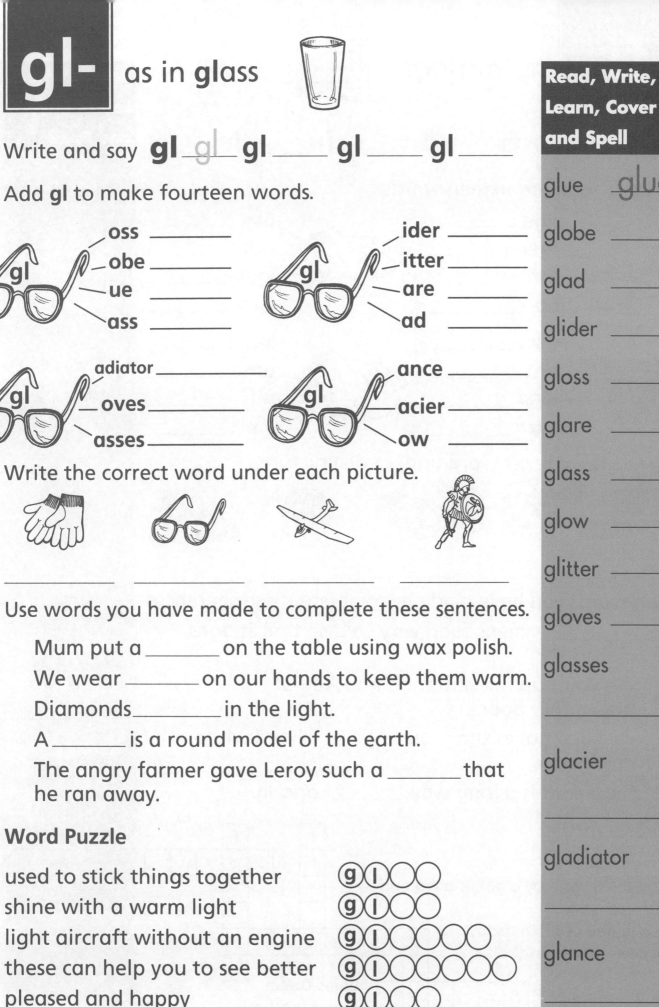

Write and say **gl** _gl_ **gl** ____ **gl** ____ **gl** ____

Add **gl** to make fourteen words.

gl oss _____	gl ider _____
obe _____	itter _____
ue _____	are _____
ass _____	ad _____
gl adiator _____	gl ance _____
oves _____	acier _____
asses _____	ow _____

Write the correct word under each picture.

_____ _____ _____ _____

Use words you have made to complete these sentences.

Mum put a _____ on the table using wax polish.

We wear _____ on our hands to keep them warm.

Diamonds _____ in the light.

A _____ is a round model of the earth.

The angry farmer gave Leroy such a _____ that he ran away.

Word Puzzle

used to stick things together   g l ○ ○ ○

shine with a warm light   g l ○ ○ ○

light aircraft without an engine   g l ○ ○ ○ ○ ○

these can help you to see better   g l ○ ○ ○ ○ ○ ○

pleased and happy   g l ○ ○ ○

used in windows   g l ○ ○ ○

a quick look   g l ○ ○ ○ ○ ○

Read, Write, Learn, Cover and Spell

glue _glue_

globe _____

glad _____

glider _____

gloss _____

glare _____

glass _____

glow _____

glitter _____

gloves _____

glasses

_____

glacier

_____

gladiator

_____

glance

_____

 **fr-** as in **fridge**

Write and say **fr** _fr_ **fr** _____ **fr** _____ **fr** _____

Add **fr** to make sixteen words.

idge _____
eezer _____
esh _____
og _____

ost _____
ock _____
inge _____
iday F _____

eckles _____
ont _____
iend _____
ighten _____

ied _____
ame _____
uit _____
om _____

Write the correct word under each picture.

_____ _____ _____ _____ _____

Use words you have made to complete these sentences.

A _____ keeps food very cold so that it does not go bad.

We went up the path and knocked at the _____ door.

_____ makes the ground go hard and white in winter.

New York is a long way _____ London.

Crossword

Clues Across
3. a dress worn by a girl or a woman
4. to cause fear
5. the day after Thursday
6. cooked in hot fat or oil in a pan on top of a stove

Clues Down
1. not tired; new
2. person you know well and like
4. a picture is often in one of these

Read, Write, Learn, Cover and Spell
frog _frog_
fridge _____
fringe _____
fruit _____
front _____
frost _____
from _____
fresh _____
friend _____
frock _____
frame _____
Friday _____
fried _____
freckles _____
freezer _____
frighten _____

6

gr- as in grin

- Write and say **gr** _gr_ **gr** _____ **gr** _____ **gr** _____

- Add **gr** to make sixteen words.

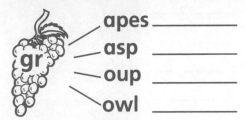

gr
- apes _____
- asp _____
- oup _____
- owl _____

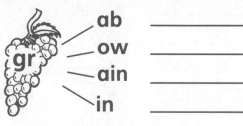

gr
- ab _____
- ow _____
- ain _____
- in _____

gr
- een _____
- avy _____
- aze _____
- unt _____

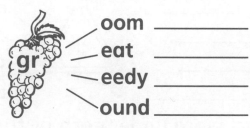

gr
- oom _____
- eat _____
- eedy _____
- ound _____

- Write the correct word under each picture.

_____ _____ _____ _____

- Use words you have made to complete these sentences.

   A puppy will _____ into a dog.

   Rod was _____ when he ate all the sweets.

   King Alfred was a _____ king.

   My mum had to _____ my dad's arm when she tripped.

   We plant seeds in the _____ .

Word Puzzle

dogs may make this noise   g r ◇ ◇ ◇

a _____ of sand   g r ◇ ◇ ◇

take hold of suddenly   g r ◇ ◇

to feed on growing grass   g r ◇ ◇ ◇

a noise like a pig   g r ◇ ◇ ◇

colour of grass   g r ◇ ◇ ◇

smile, showing your teeth   g r ◇ ◇

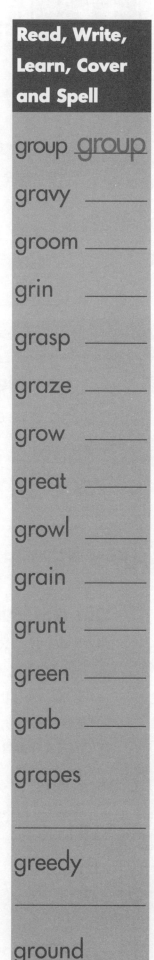

group group

gravy _____

groom _____

grin _____

grasp _____

graze _____

grow _____

great _____

growl _____

grain _____

grunt _____

green _____

grab _____

grapes
_____

greedy
_____

ground
_____

7

tr- as in trout

Write and say **tr** _tr_ **tr** _____ **tr** _____ **tr** _____

Add **tr** to make sixteen words.

tr iangle _____
amp _____
ack _____
eat _____

tr ain _____
ail _____
actor _____
ainers _____

tr apeze _____
ue _____
ip _____
emble _____

tr ee _____
ap _____
out _____
easure _____

Write the correct word under each picture. _____

_____ _____ _____ _____

Use words you have made to complete these sentences.

The _____ went fast along the railway _____ .

Our class went on a coach _____ to Conway Castle.

An old Indian _____ led to the caves.

A _____ is a very large plant with leaves, branches and a trunk.

Doctors _____ people who are ill to try to make them better.

Crossword

Clues Down
1. has 3 sides and 3 corners
2. used on farms to pull machines
4. It's _____ that 2 + 3 = 5
6. to catch your foot and fall

Clues Across
2. soft, light shoes
3. for catching animals or people
5. fish that lives in fresh water
7. to shake or shiver

Read, Write, Learn, Cover and Spell
tramp _tramp_
train _____
trip _____
trail _____
treat _____
trap _____
true _____
trout _____
track _____
tractor _____
tree _____
treasure _____
trainers _____
trapeze _____
triangle _____
tremble _____

8

 **sk-** as in **sk**ull

- Write and say **sk** _sk_ **sk** _____ **sk** _____ **sk** _____

- Add **sk** to make fifteen words.

- ull _____
- i _____
- in _____
- ip _____

- inny _____
- y _____
- irt _____
- ater _____

- etch _____
- ill _____
- id _____
- in-diver _____

- ylark _____
- eleton _____
- yscraper _____

- Write the correct word under each picture.

_____ _____ – _____ _____ _____ _____

- Use words you have made to complete these sentences.

    Pete did a very good _____ of a spaceship.
    Sally's special _____ is painting pictures of horses.
    Your body is covered with a layer of _____ .
    We saw the lorry _____ on the icy road.
    You can see clouds, rainbows and stars in the _____ .

- **Word Puzzle**

the bone of your head ⓢⓚ◯◯◯
high flying song bird ⓢⓚ◯◯◯◯◯
slide without meaning to ⓢⓚ◯◯
very thin ⓢⓚ◯◯◯◯
the bones of your body ⓢⓚ◯◯◯◯◯◯
jump with little hopping steps ⓢⓚ◯◯
a very tall building ⓢⓚ◯◯◯◯◯◯◯◯

9

Read, Write, Learn, Cover and Spell

ski _ski_

skirt _____

skater _____

sketch _____

skill _____

skin _____

skid _____

sky _____

skull _____

skip _____

skinny _____

skyscraper _____

skin-diver _____

skeleton _____

skylark _____

oy as in boy

Write and say **oy** _oy_ **oy** _____ **oy** _____ **oy** _____

Add **oy** to make twelve words.

b _____
t _____ **oy**
j _____

bu _____
enj _____ **oy**
cowb _____

v _____ age _____
r _____ **oy** _____ al _____
destr _____

ster _____
ann _____ **oy**
l _____ al _____

Write the correct word under each picture.

_____ _____ _____ _____

Use words you have made to complete these sentences.

You will often see a _____ anchored in a river to guide ships.

A _____ is something you like to play with.

Our _____ on the QE2 took us across the Atlantic Ocean.

Sam will _____ our teacher if he doesn't stop wasting time.

The Queen lives in a _____ palace.

Word Puzzle

he grows to be a man
to like to do something
a kind of shellfish
to spoil
looks after cattle in America
much happiness

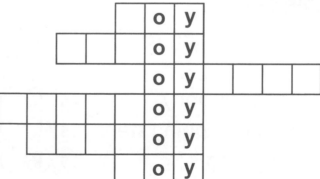

Read, Write, Learn, Cover and Spell

oyster _oyster_

buoy _____

royal _____

toy _____

annoy _____

enjoy _____

boy _____

joy _____

loyal _____

cowboy

_____

voyage

_____

destroy

_____

10

oi as in coins

- Write and say **oi** _oi_ **oi** ____ **oi** ____ **oi** ____

- Add **oi** to make sixteen words.

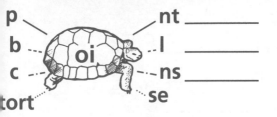

p ____ nt _____
b ____ l _____
c ____ ns _____
tort ____ se _____

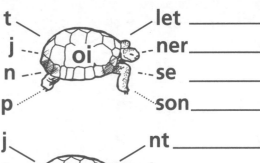

t ____ let _____
j ____ ner _____
n ____ se _____
p ____ son _____

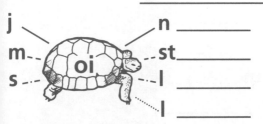

j ____ n _____
m ____ st _____
s ____ l _____
____ l _____

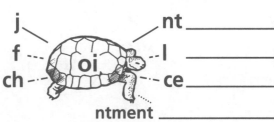

j ____ nt _____
f ____ l _____
ch ____ ce _____
____ ntment _____

- Write the correct word under each picture.

_____ _____ _____ _____ _____

- Use words you have made to complete these sentences.

  A needle has a very sharp _____.

  I couldn't hear my brother because of the
  loud _____ of his stereo.

  _____ floats on water.

  You have a _____ of vanilla, toffee or
  blueberry ice cream.

  The ankle is the _____ between the foot
  and the leg.

- **Word Puzzle**

  fasten together
  makes things with wood
  plants grow in this
  cream for sore skin or cuts
  animal with hard shell
  damp; just a little bit wet
  can kill or harm living things
  to bubble and give off steam

11

 **ur** as in n**ur**se

▶ Write and say **ur** _ur_ ur _____ ur _____ ur _____

▶ Add **ur** to make sixteen words.

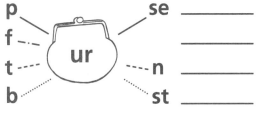

p _____ se _____
f _____ _____
t **ur** n _____
b _____ st _____

c _____ ly _____
t _____ key _____
p **ur** ple _____
m _____ der _____

Sat _____ day _____
n _____ se _____
t **ur** ban _____
Th _____ sday _____

p _____ r _____
Sat _____ n _____
t **ur** nip _____
ret _____ n _____

▶ Write the correct word under each picture.

_____ _____ _____ _____ _____

Use words you have made to complete these sentences.

The lady's bag_____ and all her shopping
fell on the floor.

Money is carried in a _____.

We don't go to school on a_____.

The teacher asked me to_____the book
to the shelf.

When it is very cold, water will _____ into ice.

Word Puzzle

sound a happy cat makes
looks after sick people
reddish blue colour
a round, white vegetable
the day after Wednesday
to give something back
to break open suddenly
to move round like a wheel

purse _purse_
curly _____
turkey _____
purple _____
nurse _____
fur _____
turnip _____
Saturn _____
turn _____
return _____
burst _____
purr _____
turban _____
Saturday _____
Thursday _____
murder _____

12

wh- as in whale

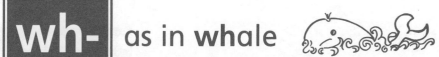

▶ Write and say **wh** _wh_ **wh** _____ **wh** _____ **wh** _____

▶ Add **wh** to make eighteen words.

(wh)
- y _____
- eel _____
- ip _____
- at _____

(wh)
- ere _____
- ich _____
- en _____
- arf _____

(wh)
- iskers _____
- ite _____
- isky _____
- eat _____
- istle _____

(wh)
- isper _____
- ale _____
- isk _____
- irl _____
- inny _____

▶ Write the correct word under each picture.

_____ _____ _____ _____ _____

▶ Use words you have made to complete these sentences.

_____ were you late for school?

_____ is your name?   _____ boy sits here?

_____ did the game start?   _____ is your book?

The _____ is the largest animal on Earth.

Ships load and unload at a _____.

▶ **Crossword**

Clues Down
1. cry made by a horse
2. flour is made from this
3. a referee of a football match uses one

Clues Across
2. to turn around and around very fast
3. speak very softly
4. very strong drink made from grain
5. colour of fresh snow

13

sl- as in sledge

Write and say **sl** ___ sl ___ sl ___ sl ___

slow _slow_

Add **sl** to make sixteen words.

- ug _____
- eep _____
- im _____
- ide _____

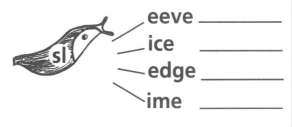
- eeve _____
- ice _____
- edge _____
- ime _____

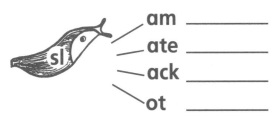
- am _____
- ate _____
- ack _____
- ot _____

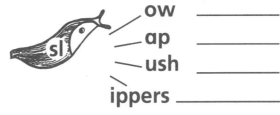
- ow _____
- ap _____
- ush _____
- ippers _____

Write the correct word under each picture.

_____ _____ _____ _____ _____

Use words you have made to complete these sentences.

Thin pieces of_____are used to cover a roof.

When you _____ a door, you shut it with a bang.

A_____is the part of clothing that covers your arm.

When you _____, you close your eyes and your body rests.

A_____slides over the ice and snow.

Word Puzzle

like a snail, but without a shell

opposite of tight

thin, not fat

not quick

melting snow

hit with hand

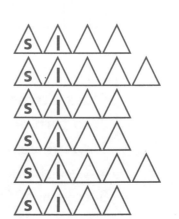

slap _____

slam _____

sleeve _____

slice _____

slug _____

slate _____

sleep _____

slush _____

slack _____

slide _____

sledge _____

slim _____

slot _____

slime _____

slippers

_____

14

-le as in beetle

• Write and say **le** _le_ **le** ____ **le** ____ **le** ____

• Add **le** to make sixteen words.

app  _____
pudd _____
catt _____
bubb _____

hand  _____
cast _____
beet _____
eag _____

bott  _____
tremb _____
steep _____
tumb _____

coup  _____
ank _____
midd _____
cand _____

• Write the correct word under each picture.

_____ _____ _____ _____ _____

• Use words you have made to complete these sentences.

A _____ holds liquids and is made from glass or plastic.

The _____ on the door is too high to reach.

The soap _____ floated away in the air.

When a _____ burns, it makes light.

An _____ is a round, crisp, juicy fruit.

• **Crossword**

Clues Across
4. to fall down
5. two things; a pair
6. small pool of dirty water

Clues Down
1. shake, shiver
2. pointed top of a church tower
3. halfway between two things

15

Read, Write, Learn, Cover and Spell

apple _apple_

tumble _____

puddle _____

bottle _____

ankle _____

eagle _____

middle _____

beetle _____

cattle _____

couple _____

bubble _____

steeple _____

castle _____

candle _____

handle _____

tremble _____

-er as in hammer

Write and say **er** _er_ **er** _____ **er** _____ **er** _____

after _after_

Add **er** to make sixteen words.

tow	_____	pap	_____
riv	_____	wait	_____
long	_____	nev	_____
aft	_____	hamm	_____

never _____

better _____

teach	_____	rul	_____
summ	_____	dang	_____
winn	_____	und	_____
bett	_____	wint	_____

winter _____

ruler _____

waiter _____

Write the correct word under each picture.

_____ _____ _____ _____ _____

tower _____

river _____

paper _____

Use words you have made to complete these sentences.

The pages of this book are made of _____.

The church bell hangs in the _____.

Cats are a _____ to the baby birds.

A _____ helps us to find out how long things are.

In _____ it is warm and the days are longer.

danger _____

under _____

winner _____

longer _____

teacher

Word Puzzle. Write the opposites of these words.

shorter ⟨△△△△⟩e⟩r⟩

always ⟨△△△△⟩e⟩r⟩

summer ⟨△△△△⟩e⟩r⟩

before ⟨△△△⟩e⟩r⟩

worse ⟨△△△△⟩e⟩r⟩

over ⟨△△△⟩e⟩r⟩

summer _____

hammer _____

are as in mare

▶ Write and say **are** are are_____ are_____ are_____

▶ Add **are** to make fifteen words.

h _____   m _____
c _____   b _____
aw _____   sp _____
sh _____   f _____

p ____ nts _____   bew _____
sc ---- ---- crow   d _____
_____   st _____
r ---- _____   sc _____

▶ Write the correct word under each picture.

_____   _____   _____   _____

▶ Use words you have made to complete these sentences.

When I got on the bus I paid my _____ to the driver.

The pandas of China are very _____ animals.

My sister, brother and I _____ the family computer.

The sign on the farmer's gate said, " _____ of the bull".

A _____ looks like a large rabbit. It can run very fast.

▶ **Word Puzzle**

look at anything for a long time △△△/r\e\

without any clothes △△/r\e\   to take a chance △△△/r\e\

to frighten △△△/r\e\   for use if needed △△△△/r\e\

not often found △△△/r\e\   to look after △△△△/r\e\

seen in fields to scare birds off the crops △△△△/r\e\△△△△

bare _bare_

share _____

care _____

rare _____

stare _____

mare _____

fare _____

dare _____

aware _____

scare _____

hare _____

spare _____

parents _____

beware _____

scarecrow _____

17

sn- as in snowman

► Write and say **sn** _sn_ **sn** _____ **sn** _____ **sn** _____

► Add **sn** to make sixteen words.

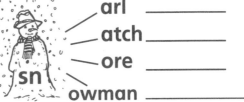
arl _____
atch _____
ore _____
owman _____

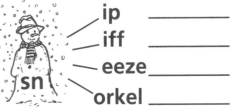
ip _____
iff _____
eeze _____
orkel _____

ooze _____
eak _____
uggle _____
ack _____

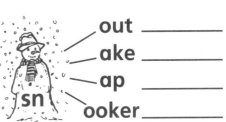
out _____
ake _____
ap _____
ooker _____

► Write the correct word under each picture.

_____ _____ _____ _____ _____

► Use words you have made to complete these sentences.

People often _____ when they have a cold.

A dog may _____ if it is angry.

Our cat likes to _____ up close to me on the settee.

My dad starts to _____ when he lies on his back.

A _____ is a long thin reptile with no legs.

► **Crossword**

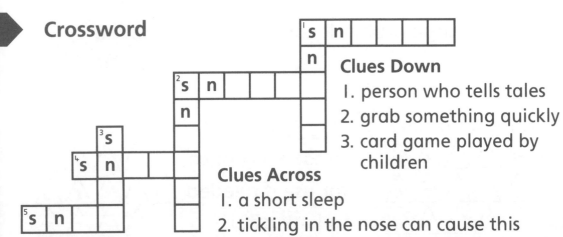

Clues Down
1. person who tells tales
2. grab something quickly
3. card game played by children

Clues Across
1. a short sleep
2. tickling in the nose can cause this
4. nose of a pig
5. cut a little bit off

Read, Write, Learn, Cover and Spell

snip _snip_

snout _____

snore _____

snap _____

snooze _____

sniff _____

sneak _____

snarl _____

snake _____

sneeze _____

snack _____

snatch _____

snorkel _____

snooker _____

snowman _____

snuggle _____

18

Add **kn** to make twelve words.

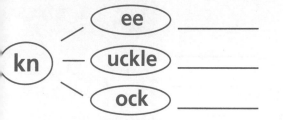

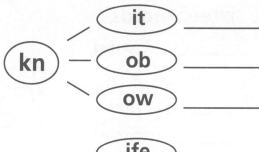

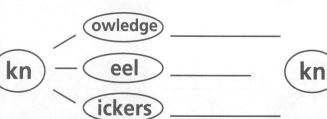

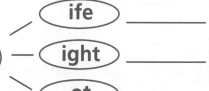

Read, Write, Learn, Cover and Spell	
knit	_knit_
knob	_____
knife	_____
knee	_____
know	_____
knot	_____
knock	_____
kneel	_____
knight	_____
knickers	_____
knuckle	_____
knowledge	_____

Write the correct word under each picture.

_____ _____ _____ _____

Use words you have made to complete these sentences.

Do you _____ the answer to that question?

A _____ is a tool that you use to cut things.

Wilma has a lot of _____ about animals.

A _____ was a man in armour who rode into battle on a horse.

Word Puzzle

the part of your leg where it bends   (k)(n)( )( )( )

short pants worn by women and girls   (k)(n)( )( )( )( )( )( )( )

hit something hard   (k)(n)( )( )( )( )

where two pieces of string are joined   (k)(n)( )( )

used to open a door or drawer   (k)(n)( )( )( )

to make wool etc into cloth using long needles   (k)(n)( )( )( )

19

-ey as in monkey

▶ Write and say **ey** __ey__ **ey** _____ **ey** _____ **ey** _____

▶ Add **ey** to make sixteen words.

barl _____   parsl _____

jock _____   kidn _____

hon _____   jers _____

donk _____   monk _____

abb _____   troll _____

vall _____   mon _____

hock _____   all _____

turk _____   chimn _____

▶ Write the correct word under each picture.

_____ _____ _____ _____ _____

▶ Use words you have made to complete these sentences.

Lots of people eat_____at Christmas.

Bees make _____which is a sweet and sticky food.

Smoke from a fire goes up through a _____.

An_____ is a place where nuns or monks live.

A _____is used to carry shopping
in a supermarket.

Word Puzzle

used for buying and selling

rides a horse in a race

green herb used in cooking

lowland between hills and mountains

another name for an ass

a very narrow street

				e	y
				e	y
				e	y
				e	y
				e	y
				e	y

20

Read, Write, Learn, Cover and Spell

jockey *jockey*

trolley _____

hockey _____

barley _____

honey _____

turkey _____

abbey _____

jersey _____

valley _____

money _____

donkey _____

alley _____

parsley _____

kidney _____

monkey _____

_____

chimney _____

Silent **b** as in com**b**

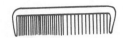

▶ Add **b** to make fifteen words.

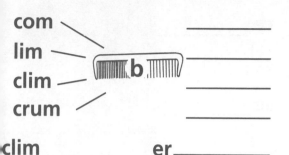

com _____   bom _____
lim _____   lam _____
clim _____   thum _____
crum _____   dum _____

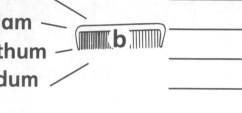

clim ___er_____   num _____
dou ___t _____   tom _____
de ___t _____
plum ___er_____   honeycom _____

▶ Write the correct word under each picture.

_____   _____   _____   _____   _____

▶ Use words you have made to complete these sentences.

You use a _____ to keep your hair tidy.

You have a _____ and four fingers on each hand.

A _____ can cause much damage and loss of life.

A _____ mended two leaking pipes.

If you are in _____ , you owe something.

Crossword

Clues Down
1. a young sheep
2. to feel not sure about something
3. a tiny bit of bread or cake

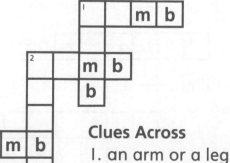

Clues Across
1. an arm or a leg
2. not able to speak
3. go up, such as a ladder
4. not able to feel anything
5. place where a dead person is buried

tomb _tomb_

thumb _____

comb _____

debt _____

limb _____

lamb _____

dumb _____

climb _____

bomb _____

numb _____

doubt _____

crumb _____

plumber _____

climber _____

honeycomb _____

ui

Read, Write, Learn, Cover and Spell

▶ Add **ui** to make fourteen words.

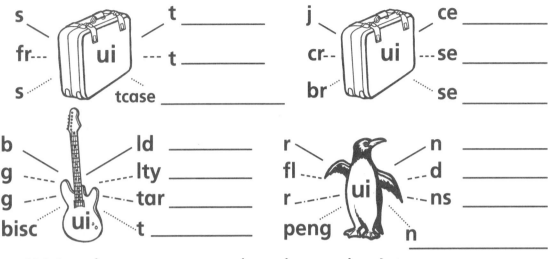

s_____ t_____   j_____ce _____
fr---**ui** ---t_____   cr---**ui**---se _____
s.....tcase _____   br.....se _____

b_____ld _____   r_____n _____
g---_____lty _____   fl---**ui**---d _____
g---**ui**---tar _____   r---.....ns _____
bisc_____t _____   peng_____n _____

▶ Write the correct word under each picture.

_____ _____ _____ _____ _____

▶ Use words you have made to complete these sentences.

We can squeeze an orange to get the _____ .

The robber was found_____of
stealing the money.

Bricklayers _____walls.

If more heavy rain falls it will_____our sports day.

Brian has a_____on his arm where
the cricket ball hit him.

Crossword

Clues Down

1. what is left of a very old building
3. a thin, small cake baked hard
4. this bird swims but can't fly

Clues Across

2. holiday on a big ship
5. for carrying clothes – such as
   when going on holiday
6. water is this – it will flow
7. a peach is a soft, juicy_____ .

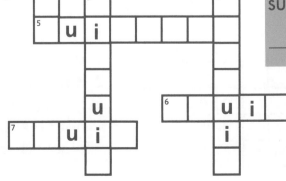

Read, Write, Learn, Cover and Spell

fruit _fruit_

cruise _____

guitar _____

suit _____

guilty _____

juice _____

build _____

ruin _____

bruise _____

ruins _____

fluid _____

penguin _____

_____

biscuit _____

_____

suitcase _____

_____

22

 **nn** as in ke**nn**el

◆ Write and say **nn**___ **nn**_____ **nn**_____ **nn**_____ **nn**_____

◆ Add **nn** to make sixteen words.

fu — el _____
te — is _____
tu — el _____
ke — el _____

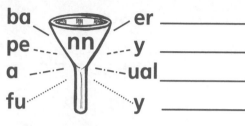

ba — er _____
pe — y _____
a — ual _____
fu — y _____

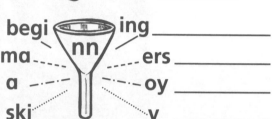

begi — ing _____
ma — ers _____
a — oy _____
ski — y _____

wi — er _____
ca — ot _____
ca — on _____
su — y _____

cannon _____

banner _____

annual _____

funny _____

◆ Write the correct word under each picture.

_____ _____ _____ _____ _____

tennis _____

kennel _____

annoy _____

◆ Use words you have made to complete these sentences.

penny _____

We were late and missed the _____ of the film.

winner _____

If I play loud music it will_____my dad.

sunny _____

We have our_____ sports day in July.

It is bad_____to talk with your mouth full.

cannot _____

Meg is ill in bed so she_____go to school today.

funnel _____

Word Puzzle

skinny _____

makes you laugh

chimney of a ship

make someone angry

beginning _____

a large, heavy gun

a small coin

_____

game played with rackets

manners _____

underground passage

_____

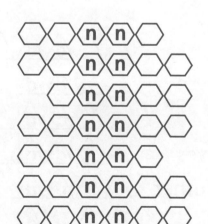

dd as in we**dd**ing

Write and say **dd**___ dd___ **dd**_____ **dd**_____ **dd**_____

Add **dd** to make fifteen words.

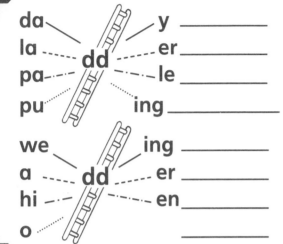

da __ y _____
la __ **dd** __ er _____
pa __ le _____
pu __ ing _____

sa __ le _____
a __ **dd** __ ress _____
ha __ ock _____
to __ ler _____

we __ ing _____
a __ **dd** __ er _____
hi __ en _____
o _____

mi __ le _____
wa __ **dd** __ le _____
su __ enly _____

Write the correct word under each picture.

_____ _____ _____ _____ _____

Use words you have made to complete these sentences.

A _____ is a seat for a rider of a horse.

Mum has _____ my sweets and I can't find them.

When you _____ you walk in shallow water.

There is a white line in the _____ of the road.

A _____ is a sweet food that you eat at the end of a meal.

Word Puzzle

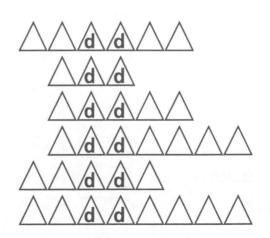

move like a duck   △ △ d d △ △

strange, unusual   △ d d

poisonous snake   △ d d △

where a person lives   △ d d △ △ △

child's name for father   △ △ d d △

happening quickly   △ △ d d △ △ △

Read, Write, Learn, Cover and Spell

paddle _paddle_

hidden _____

saddle _____

toddler _____

ladder _____

waddle _____

middle _____

odd _____

adder _____

daddy _____

address _____

haddock _____

pudding _____

suddenly _____

wedding _____

24

tt as in kitten

Write and say **tt** __tt__ **tt** _____ **tt** _____ **tt** _____

Add **tt** to make eighteen words.

bu_____on _____   bo_____le _____
bu_____er _____   mu_____er _____
ke_____le _____   a_____ic _____
ro_____en _____   co_____age _____

ba_____ery _____   ki_____en _____
pre_____y _____   ca_____le _____
li_____le _____   bi_____er _____
be_____er _____   o_____er _____
bo_____om _____   le_____uce _____

Write the correct word under each picture.

_____ _____ _____ _____ _____

Use words you have made to complete these sentences.

Gary needs a new _____ for his radio.
Farm animals such as cows, bulls
and calves are _____.
_____ is made from milk and we can
spread it on bread.
An _____ is the space or room in the roof
of a house.

Crossword

Clues Across

1. used for fastening clothes
2. eaten in salads
4. speak or grumble in
   a low voice
5. going bad or gone bad

Clues Down

1. opposite of top
2. opposite of big   3. nice to look at

kettle __kettle__

attic _____

button _____

otter _____

bitter _____

rotten _____

mutter _____

little _____

better _____

lettuce _____

butter _____

cattle _____

pretty _____

kitten _____

bottle _____

battery _____

_____

bottom _____

_____

cottage _____

_____

25

 **ll** as in holly

Write and say **ll** _____ **ll** _____ **ll** _____ **ll** _____

Add **ll** to make sixteen words.

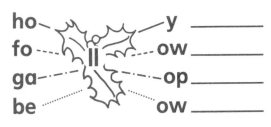

ho___y _____
fo___ow _____
ga___op _____
be___ow _____

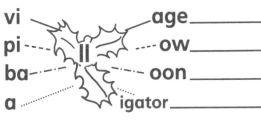

vi___age _____
pi___ow _____
ba___oon _____
a___igator _____

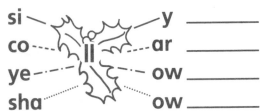

si___y _____
co___ar _____
ye___ow _____
sha___ow _____

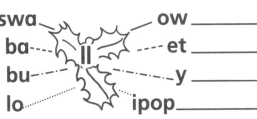

swa___ow _____
ba___et _____
bu___y _____
lo___ipop _____

Write the correct word under each picture.

_____   _____   _____   _____   _____

Use words you have made to complete these sentences.

_____has green, prickly leaves and red berries.

The horses began to _____across the field.

The flowers of a buttercup are_____.

I am still learning to swim so I stay at the_____end of the pool.

Our dog has a_____round his neck.

Crossword

Clues Down
1. to roar like an angry bull
2. to go after
4. being stupid; foolish

Clues Across
1. person who hurts and frightens other people
3. similar to a crocodile
5. you rest your head on this in bed
6. colour of a banana

26

rr as in ba**rr**ow

Write and say **rr**___ _rr_ **rr**_____ **rr**_____ **rr**_____

Add **rr** to make sixteen words.

be___y _____
mi___or _____
ca___ot _____
na___ow _____

cu___y _____
ma___y _____
bo___ow _____
tomo___ow _____

ba___ow _____
fe___y _____
wo___y _____
spa___ow _____

hu___y _____
lo___y _____
ca___y _____
me___y _____

Write the correct word under each picture.

_____ _____ _____ _____ _____

Use words you have made to complete these sentences.

Today is Monday so_____ is Tuesday.

I am going to the library to_____some books.

Jumbo jets can_____more than 400 passengers.

Mum and dad_____if I am late coming home.

Tessa is going to_____her boyfriend in June.

Word Puzzle

fruit from a tree or bush   ◯◯ r r ◯

you can see yourself in this   ◯◯ r r ◯◯

very happy and jolly   ◯◯ r r ◯

not wide   ◯◯ r r ◯◯

move quickly   ◯◯ r r ◯

hot, spicy food   ◯◯ r r ◯

a small cart that you can push   ◯◯ r r ◯◯

27

el as in mod**el**

Write and say **el** _el_ **el** _____ **el** _____ **el** _____

Add **el** to make sixteen words.

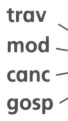 

tins	_____
jew	_____
cru	_____
kenn	_____

trow	_____
fu	_____
host	_____
lev	_____

trav	_____
mod	_____
canc	_____
gosp	_____

tunn	_____
cam	_____
chis	_____
chap	_____

Write the correct word under each picture.

_____ _____ _____ _____ _____

Use words you have made to complete these sentences.

Our car stopped because it ran out of_____ .

I was ill so mum had to _____ my music lesson.

Engineers built a_____through the mountain.

We used _____when we decorated
the Christmas tree.

The builders used a _____to shape the stone.

Crossword

Clues Down

1. a valuable, precious stone
2. a desert animal
3. smooth and flat

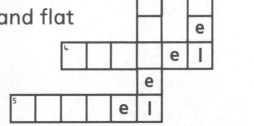

Clues Across

2. very unkind
4. move from place to place
5. shelter for a dog

Read, Write, Learn, Cover and Spell

tinsel _tinsel_

trowel _____

travel _____

tunnel _____

fuel _____

jewel _____

model _____

camel _____

cruel _____

hostel _____

cancel _____

chisel _____

chapel_____

level _____

gospel _____

_____

kennel _____

_____

bb as in ru**bb**ish

Write and say **bb** bb **bb**_____ **bb**_____ **bb**_____

Add **bb** to make fourteen words.

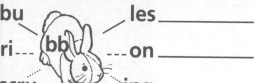

bu____les _____
ri____on _____
scru____ing _____

ru____er _____
pe____les _____
ra____it _____

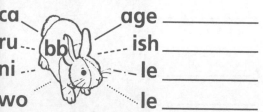

ca____age _____
ru____ish _____
ni____le _____
wo____le _____

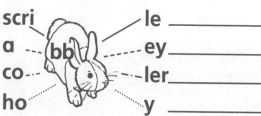

scri____le _____
a____ey _____
co____ler _____
ho____y _____

Write the correct word under each picture.

_____ _____ _____ _____

Use words you have made to complete these sentences.

A _____ repairs shoes.

A _____ is used to rub out pencil marks.

A _____ has soft fur, long ears and a short tail.

The old man began to _____, then he fell.

You will see _____ on a beach.

Word Puzzle

it is put in a dustbin

worn in the hair

you may have one in your spare time

to eat in small bites

a green vegetable

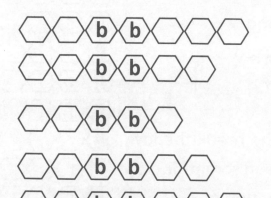

ribbon _ribbon_

bubbles _____

rubber _____

abbey _____

pebbles _____

rubbish _____

scribble _____

wobble _____

rabbit _____

nibble _____

hobby _____

cobbler _____

cabbage

_____

scrubbing

_____

29

pr- as in prawn

Write and say **pr** __pr__ **pr** _____ **pr** _____ **pr** _____

Add **pr** to make sixteen words.

pr
- ess _____
- am _____
- op _____
- esent _____

pr
- ick _____
- iest _____
- ay _____
- oblem _____

pr
- ison _____
- ince _____
- awn _____
- etty _____

pr
- imrose _____
- opeller _____
- imary _____
- esident _____

Write the correct word under each picture.

_____ _____ _____ _____ _____

Use words you have made to complete these sentences.

We have a _____ with our cat. She won't come in at night.

The United States of America has a _____ .

Something that is _____ is nice to look at.

A _____ school is usually for children up to eleven years of age.

Babies and young children are pushed in a _____ .

Word Puzzle

it holds up the washing line	p r ◇ ◇
to push on something	p r ◇ ◇ ◇
son of a King or Queen	p r ◇ ◇ ◇ ◇
a gift to someone	p r ◇ ◇ ◇ ◇ ◇
talk to God	p r ◇ ◇
place for people who break the law	p r ◇ ◇ ◇ ◇
to make a tiny hole in something	p r ◇ ◇ ◇
a small, pale yellow flower	p r ◇ ◇ ◇ ◇ ◇ ◇

30

Read, Write, Learn, Cover and Spell

pretty _pretty_

present _____

pram _____

prawn _____

prop _____

priest _____

press _____

pray _____

prince _____

prick _____

prison _____

primary

_____

propeller

_____

president

_____

primrose

_____

problem

_____

Silent **h** as in w**h**eel

Add **h** to make sixteen words.

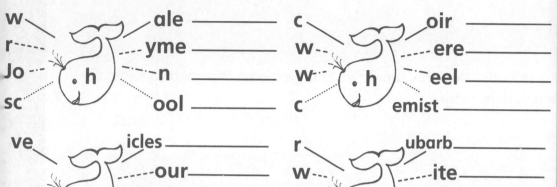

w ____ ale _____
r ____ yme _____
Jo ____ n _____
sc ____ ool _____

c ____ oir _____
w ____ ere _____
w ____ eel _____
c ____ emist _____

ve ____ icles _____
____ our _____
____ eir _____
____ onest _____

r ____ ubarb _____
w ____ ite _____
ec ____ o _____
r ____ inoceros _____

Write the correct word under each picture.

_____ _____ _____ _____

Use words you have made to complete these sentences.

A wheelbarrow usually has one _____.

Cars, lorries and buses are kinds of _____.

The person who will become
King or Queen is _____ to the throne.

You often hear an _____ in a cave or a tunnel.

A _____ is a place where children go to learn.

Crossword

Clues Across

2. large, African animal with thick skin
5. a boy's name
6. opposite of black
7. sixty minutes

Clues Down

1. group of people who sing together
3. not stealing, cheating or telling lies
4. stems of this plant are cooked and eaten

Schofield & Sims

the long-established educational publisher
specialising in maths, English and science materials for schools

Key Spelling is a series of books containing puzzles and problems designed to reinforce essential spelling skills and knowledge.

Key Spelling Book 2 includes:

- Vowel sounds made by more than one letter (e.g. 'ui' and 'oy')
- Letter blends such as 'gl', 'fr' and 'sk'
- 'wh' digraph
- Word endings (e.g. _er and _are)
- Silent letters (e.g. 'b' in comb)

This book would be suitable for children in Key Stage 2.

The full range of titles in the series is as follows:

Key Spelling Book 1:   ISBN 978 07217 0841 6

Key Spelling Book 2:   ISBN 978 07217 0842 3

Key Spelling Book 3:   ISBN 978 07217 0843 0

Key Spelling Book 4:   ISBN 978 07217 0844 7

Have you tried *Springboard* by Schofield & Sims?
This is a progressive series of books reinforcing key aspects of literacy such as sentence construction, vocabulary and reading comprehension.

**For further information and to place your order
visit www.schofieldandsims.co.uk or telephone 01484 607080**

ISBN 978-07217-0842-3

9 780721 708423

Schofield & Sims

Dogley Mill, Fenay Bridge, Huddersfield HD8 0NQ
Phone: 01484 607080 Facsimile: 01484 606815
E-mail: sales@schofieldandsims.co.uk
www.schofieldandsims.co.uk

ISBN 978 07217 0842 3

£2.45
(Retail price)

Key Stage 2
Age range: 7–11 years